THIS BOOK
BE**LONG**S TO

....

Published by Sweet Cherry Publishing Limited
Unit 36, Vulcan House, Vulcan Road,
Leicester, LE5 3EF, United Kingdom

Published in 2020
2 4 6 8 10 9 7 5 3 1
ISBN: 978-1-78226-767-6

Printed and manufactured in Turkey (T.L010)

Made under licence by
Sweet Cherry Publishing Limited
Written by Dan Metcalf
www.sweetcherrypublishing.com

The Illuminated Film Company Limited 2020
Created/Directed by Edward Foster
Produced by Iain Harvey

the Rubbish World of... DAVE SPUD™

CONTENTS

Dave

Gareth

Are we there yet?

This is not rubbish

I have a plan

Dave

Fuzzypeg

WELCOME!
Ey up you lot. This is the weird, funny, crazy and completely RUBBISH world of Dave Spud! If you ever wanted to find out more about Grimsby's own magnet for disaster, then you've come to the right place. Inside these grubby pages we've got stories, puzzles, pictures and more fun facts than you can shake a sausage at. So pull your wellies on, grab an extra pair of pants and hop into Gran's camper. Prepare for a truly RUBBISH adventure!

Ha ha! Dave's bum!

This should prove entertaining...

OH BUM

↑ I dare you to lick this doughnut.

IT WASN'T ME!

FACT FILE

NAME: Dave Spud

PET: Fuzzypeg

FAVOURITE SCHOOL SUBJECT: Lunch. Or maybe home time...

FAVOURITE HOBBY: Eating. Hanging out with friends.

FAVOURITE FOOD: Mum's toad-in-the-hole and bangers and mash.

FAVOURITE SPORT: Pudding snorkeling (There's REALLY not much to do in Grimsby.)

WHO FARTED? Err...

DID YOU KNOW? Gran says Dave looks just like a French bulldog chewing a wasp!

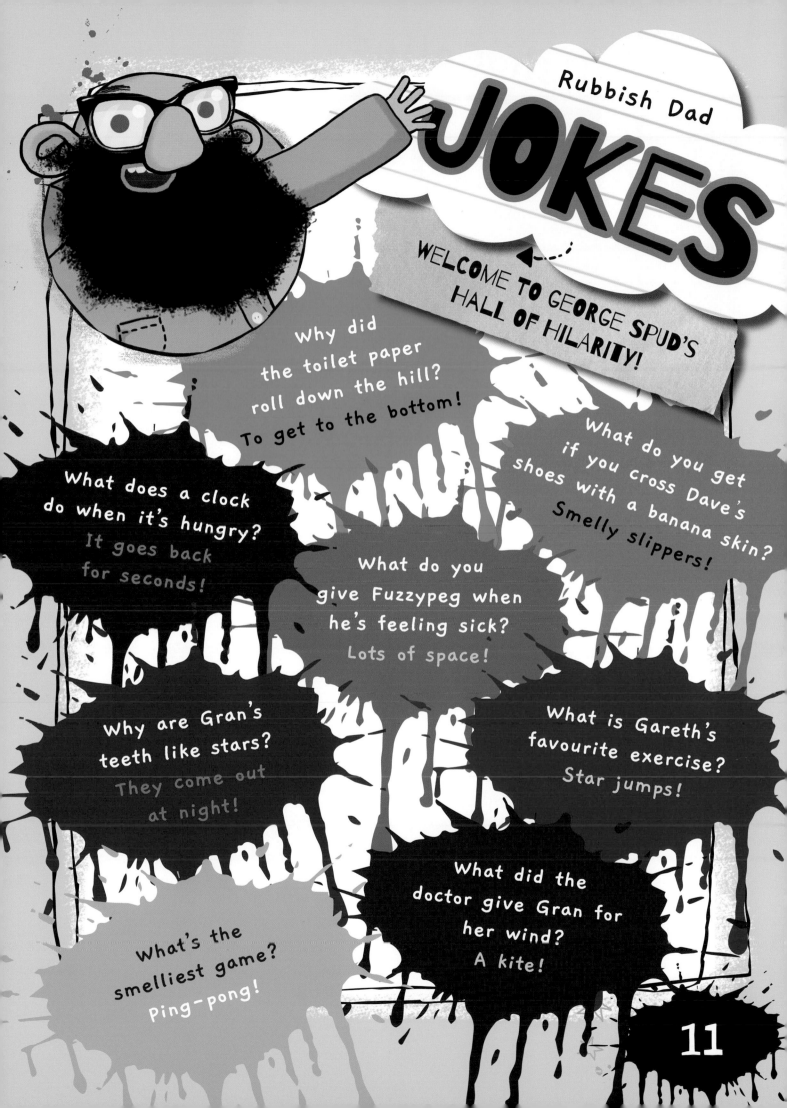

Rubbish Dad

JOKES

WELCOME TO GEORGE SPUD'S HALL OF HILARITY!

Why did the toilet paper roll down the hill?
To get to the bottom!

What do you get if you cross Dave's shoes with a banana skin?
Smelly slippers!

What does a clock do when it's hungry?
It goes back for seconds!

What do you give Fuzzypeg when he's feeling sick?
Lots of space!

Why are Gran's teeth like stars?
They come out at night!

What is Gareth's favourite exercise?
Star jumps!

What's the smelliest game?
Ping-pong!

What did the doctor give Gran for her wind?
A kite!

11

A Starfish Called GARETH

That's me!

GET YA GEAR, GRAB A GRANNY – EVERYONE IN THE CAMPER!

1 DONKEY BRAINS! Dave was fed up of losing at video games. Luckily, Mum told everyone to get packing. They were going on holiday!

2 The holiday got off to a bad start when the camper was filled with something that smelt like a dinosaur had farted! Fuzzypeg had eaten all the food out of the cool-box. He was filling up with fart gas and was about to EXPLODE!

3 When the Spuds settled down for dinner, they found Fuzzypeg had eaten everything but the tinned veg! Hungry and bored, the Spuds went to bed. Dave and Anna challenged each other to a maggot race in their sleeping bags.

THIS IS THE LIFE.

I hear trouble calling.

4 The rocking of the camper made the ground shake. Then the entire cliff side crumbled, tipping the van down into the cold sea!

Poor Fuzzypeg!

Anna

THIS IS YOUR FAULT DAVE!

1000M

2000M

4000M

5 Down they went, deeper and deeper. At 2000 metres deep, no light could get through from the surface. At 4000 metres, the pressure made their voices seriously weird. Then the van hit the ocean bed.

6 Dave offered to go for help, and he set out in Anna's wheelchair. As he whizzed along, he noticed a starfish stuck on his armrest. He named it Gareth.

7 Dave kept going, but ran over a long, squishy purple thing. It was a giant octopus tentacle! The sea monster grabbed him. The only thing Dave could find to help him was a can of peas.

Hero schmeeero...

8 Dave threw it right at the octopus. He missed. RUBBISH!. But it didn't matter. The octopus dropped Dave and chased after the tin. It was like a big dog, really.

I HAVE A PLAN.

9 When he got to the surface, Dave played arcade games with Gareth. They bought chips and a doughnut. When they ran out of money, Dave remembered that he still needed to save his family.

10 He sailed out on a fishing boat and pulled the campervan up to the surface. The Spud family shouted in glee and whooped for joy. Dave the hero! Then they saw his doughnut and chips.

HAPPY HOLIDAYS DAVE!

11 Dad was so mad that he grounded Dave for the rest of the holiday. BUM! Ah, well. It wasn't so bad being grounded, especially with a video-game playing starfish to hang out with!

WHO YOU LOOKING AT?

One of the twins has got hold of Dad's telescope. But, who they are spying on?

1

2

Answer:..

Answer:..

3

4

Answer:..

Answer:..

16

5

Answer: ....

6

Answer: ....

7

Answer: ....

8

Answer: ....

9

Answer: ....

17

The answers are on P68

meet ANNA SPUD

BORN TO RIDE

FACT FILE

NAME: Anna Spud
FAVOURITE BROTHER: Dave
LEAST FAVOURITE BROTHER: Dave
FAVOURITE FOOD: Chips!
REALLY GOOD AT: Popping a wheelie.
REALLY BAD AT: Stairs
LIKES: Chips!
DISLIKES: Losing
AMBITION: Become an awesome stuntwoman - or just eat CHIPS!
FAVOURITE ACTIVITY: Hanging out with her friends at the dump.

ANNA SPUD

BUMBAG!

18

DID YOU KNOW?
Anna can play the triangle. Badly.

DOT-TO-DOT

Something strange is happening in the skies of Grimsby. Join the dots to find out what.

whoooosh

CRIKEY I CAN'T SEE A THING WITHOUT MY GLASSES.

The answers are on P68

19

DAVE
STEP by STEP

Spud head

Follow the steps to draw Dave in all his rubbish glory. His hair and shoes are already done!

1

Dave's head looks like a spud with ears.

2

This spud needs a jumper.

3

Dave's hands look like sausages...

4

...and his trousers have skinny little legs.

5

20

Draw Dave's eyebrows, eyes and nose.

6

Add his grumpy down-turned mouth.

7

Now colour Dave in!

Draw me in this space.

NO GRUMPY FACES!

GET YA GEAR, GRAB A GRANNY – EVERYONE IN THE CAMPER!

Betty

DID YOU KNOW? Betty was the Bog-Roll Champion 1987!

meet BETTY SPUD

FACT FILE

NAME: Betty Spud
OCCUPATION: Driving trucks. Give her an eighteen-wheeler and a long stretch of motorway and she'll be as happy as Larry!
FAVOURITE HOLIDAY DESTINATION: Grimsby service station.
FAVOURITE SNACK: Tea and toast.
BEST ADVICE: When life gets you down, stick on the radio and have a disco!

Twin

ODD ONES OUT

Double bum!

Oh no! Where are the real Dave and Anna? Use the clues to eliminate the imposters. Cross them off as you go and find the real Spuds.

CLUES

1. Dave has hair.
2. Anna doesn't wear yellow trainers.
3. Dave definitely would not wear blue trousers.
4. Only an imposter would wear a yellow tie.
6. Dave loathes red shoes.
5. Anna's wheels are not blue.
7. Anna loves her hair clip.
8. Dave thinks hair clips are rubbish

S'not fair

The answers are on P68

23

PUZZLED?

Oh bum! Fuzzypeg ran into the coffee table and knocked these puzzle pieces out of place. Can you work out where they're meant to go?

24

The answers are on P68

PIXEL ART

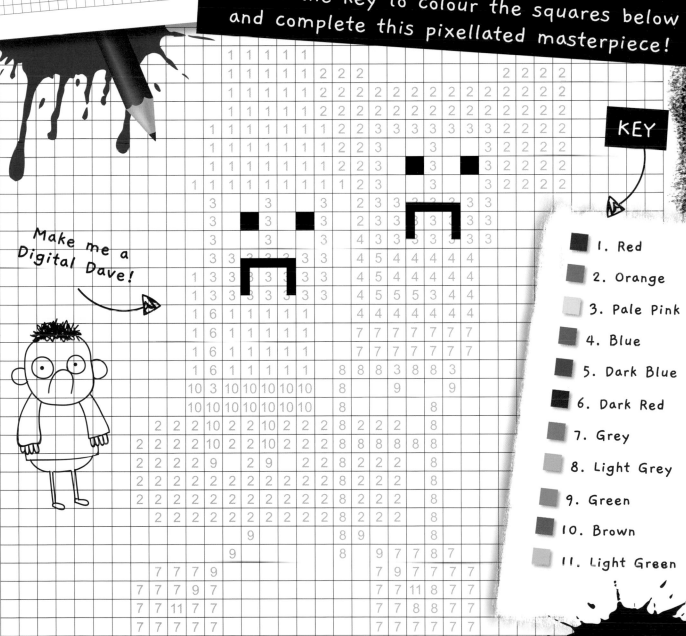

Dave and Anna have always wanted to be inside a computer game! Each number has a corresponding colour in the key below. Follow the key to colour the squares below and complete this pixellated masterpiece!

Make me a Digital Dave!

KEY

1. Red
2. Orange
3. Pale Pink
4. Blue
5. Dark Blue
6. Dark Red
7. Grey
8. Light Grey
9. Green
10. Brown
11. Light Green

25

THE COAT OF DOOM

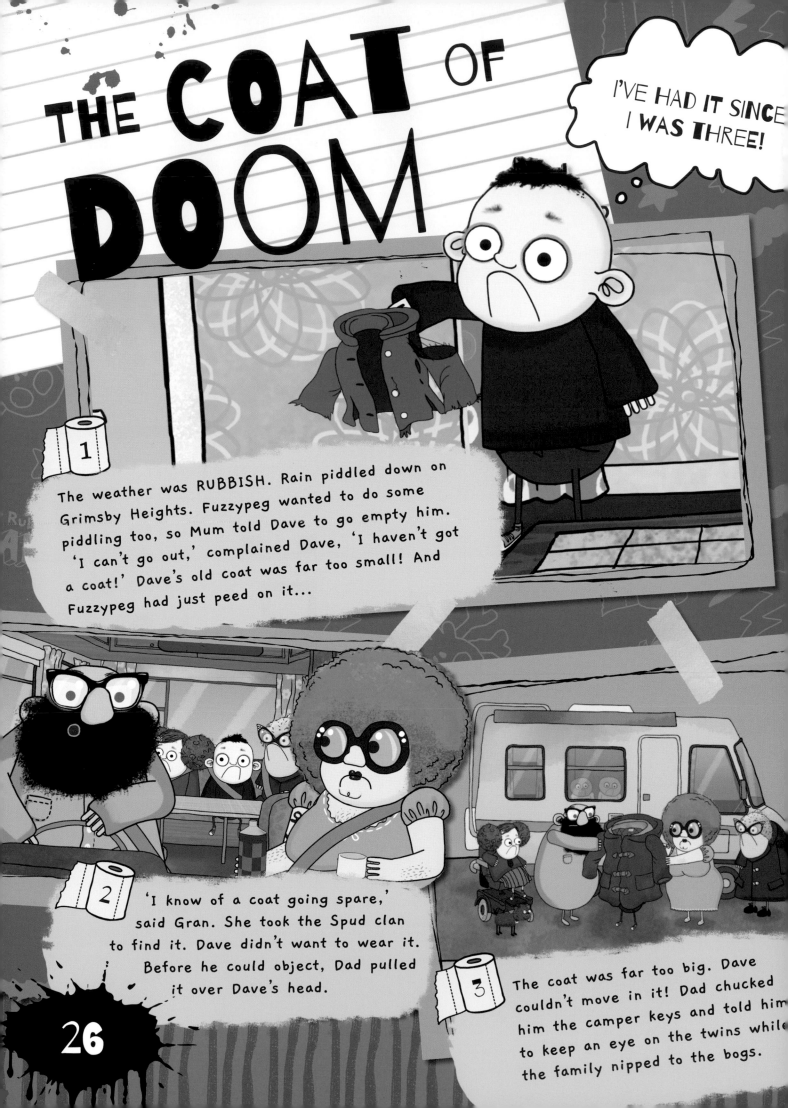

I'VE HAD IT SINCE I WAS THREE!

1 The weather was RUBBISH. Rain piddled down on Grimsby Heights. Fuzzypeg wanted to do some piddling too, so Mum told Dave to go empty him. 'I can't go out,' complained Dave, 'I haven't got a coat!' Dave's old coat was far too small! And Fuzzypeg had just peed on it...

2 'I know of a coat going spare,' said Gran. She took the Spud clan to find it. Dave didn't want to wear it. Before he could object, Dad pulled it over Dave's head.

3 The coat was far too big. Dave couldn't move in it! Dad chucked him the camper keys and told him to keep an eye on the twins while the family nipped to the bogs.

26

4

Dave heard the twins lock the camper door. Oh, BUM! Then, out of nowhere, a brutal wind blew a crow into Dave's face. The coat's hood slammed shut, trapping Dave and the crow.

5

The coat was bigger on the inside than the outside! Dave fell deeper and deeper into it. Double BUM!

6

When the rest of the family returned, Dave was stuck inside the coat. Mum flung it upside down. Dave tumbled through the fabric universe like a skydiver. Then, with a SPLAT he landed in gooey patch of old bubble-gum.

BIG FAT HAIRY KNICKERS

7 Suddenly, Dave had an idea. He shouted to his family: 'Try flushing me out!' The Spud family leapt into action. They pushed a pipe down the sleeve of the coat and let it RIP!

8 Dave heard a gurgle of water, then he was washed through the coat. He emerged in a stinky bog that had to be the armpit.

9 Dad went to check on the twins, and heard the sound of the camper engine vroooom into life. They needed the van keys, NOW! Thinking quickly, Mum stuck the coat under a hand dryer. WHOOOOOOSH! Dave's head popped out of the sleeve, but the rest of him was stuck.

10 It was Anna's turn to think fast! She rummaged through a cupboard and came back with a vacuum cleaner and wicked grin on her face. Gran turned the ancient vacuum up a coat sleeve. With a SCREAM, Dave was pulled into the vacuum's dust bag.

11 Mum pulled on the bag's zip. Dave threw the van keys to Dad, who LEAPT onto the passing camper and stopped it.

12 The Spud family drove happily home. Dave was free of the coat of doom but was now sluck inside the vacuum cleaner. Oh well! At least his old coat fitted him again. Even if it did smell slightly of dog wee...

29

meet
GEORGE SPUD

Scotch egg anyone?

FACT FILE

NAME: George Spud
OCCUPATION: Working down at the dump. It's a cracking place to get free stuff from.
FAVOURITE HOBBY: Inventing and fixing stuff.
FAVOURITE FOOD: Cheese. Especially free cheese.
IDEAL DAY: Sitting down with a cup of tea, a bit of telly and a spot of DIY.

CAN'T BEAT A BOGOF!*

30

*Buy one, get one free!

SPOT THE DIFFERENCE

Someone's been fiddling with the family photos (I blame Dave). Can you find the 13 differences between the two pictures?

Everything smells like farts!

The answers are on P68

31

HELP DAVE ESCAPE!

(GOOD LUCK)

We Spuds do NOT leave each other behind.

LOOK AND

It's mayhem in Grimsby today! Can you help Dave find a[l]
this picture?

FIND

things on the list in

GRAN ●
THE TWINS ●
GARETH ●
FUZZYPEG ●
BETTY ●
GEORGE ●
CAMPER ●
ROBERT ROBOT ●
A **DISCAR**DED APPLE **CORE** ●
13 PACKS OF PINK LOO ROLL ●
5 **INDIVI**DUAL WHITE LOO ROLLS ●
4 PAIRS OF UNDERWEAR ●

The answers are on P68

Bagsy the toilet first!

DAVE

BANANA

stinks of lavender

meet GRAN

FACT FILE

NAME: Gran

FAVOURITE PLACE: Sunbathing down at the Grimsby docks.

FAVOURITE FAMILY ADVENTURE: The time Dave got stuck in her old abandoned coat!

FAVOURITE FOOD: Pie with jam roly-poly and extra gravy.

BEST ADVICE: Life sometimes IS rubbish, you just gotta DO IT WITH GUSTO!

DID YOU KNOW? Gran is so old, even her wrinkles have wrinkles!

FIND THEM!

Gran's lost her teeth again and it's Anna's turn to help find them! First find the words in the wordsearch, then note down any letters where the words cross. These should spell out where the missing teeth are! Ew!

DAVE • GRIMSBY • FART • BETTY
GEORGE • CHIPS • GARETH • SMELLY
GRAN • FLASK • SCOTCH EGG • FUZZYPEG

J G E P G R A N V C T G Q R N D D F W Z G M E A
U O V M E C X L A Q V R T Z Z U F D J V C B F W
Y L L T D H E P U C H I P S H I C P S O V T U D
Y T J P I I C A H P R M W H W E C Q C E V F Z P
P Y U E R S Q X D B X S D S S E G R O E G H Z H
O M E B Y D D A V E J B A G R F A R T B G O Y E
H E D G L D M Q H T E Y C K I P S X C R Y C P D
F K S A L F H V H T E R A G M E G V H I G S E Z
B C Y K E T T P U Y W D I P S P P A E C H L G K
T S G G M V K G U R L H L V B D L E G U T G Z Q
I V O O S B I U U M G T W R Y O V I G M I P M R
F K X J L Z G D H G A U J H F S Z D E R M Y M T
O X W J E R X T S L H X S G R U U M A S N Q U X

The answers are on P68

37

meet GARETH

A talking starfish? I bet you're trouble...

FACT FILE

NAME: Gareth (even though I'm a girl!)

BEST MATE: Dave Spud, of course!

FAVOURITE HOBBY: Playing video games.

LIKES: Chilling with my bestie, Dave.

DISLIKES: Sushi

REALLY GOOD AT: Explaining what's going on.

REALLY BAD AT: Staying out of trouble.

MOST UNUSUAL FEATURE: Being a talking starfish!

WHAT CAN POSSIBLY GO WRONG?!

DID YOU KNOW? Starfish aren't really fish and have an eye at the end of each of their arms.

38

Cover me in whelks and call me Delilah!

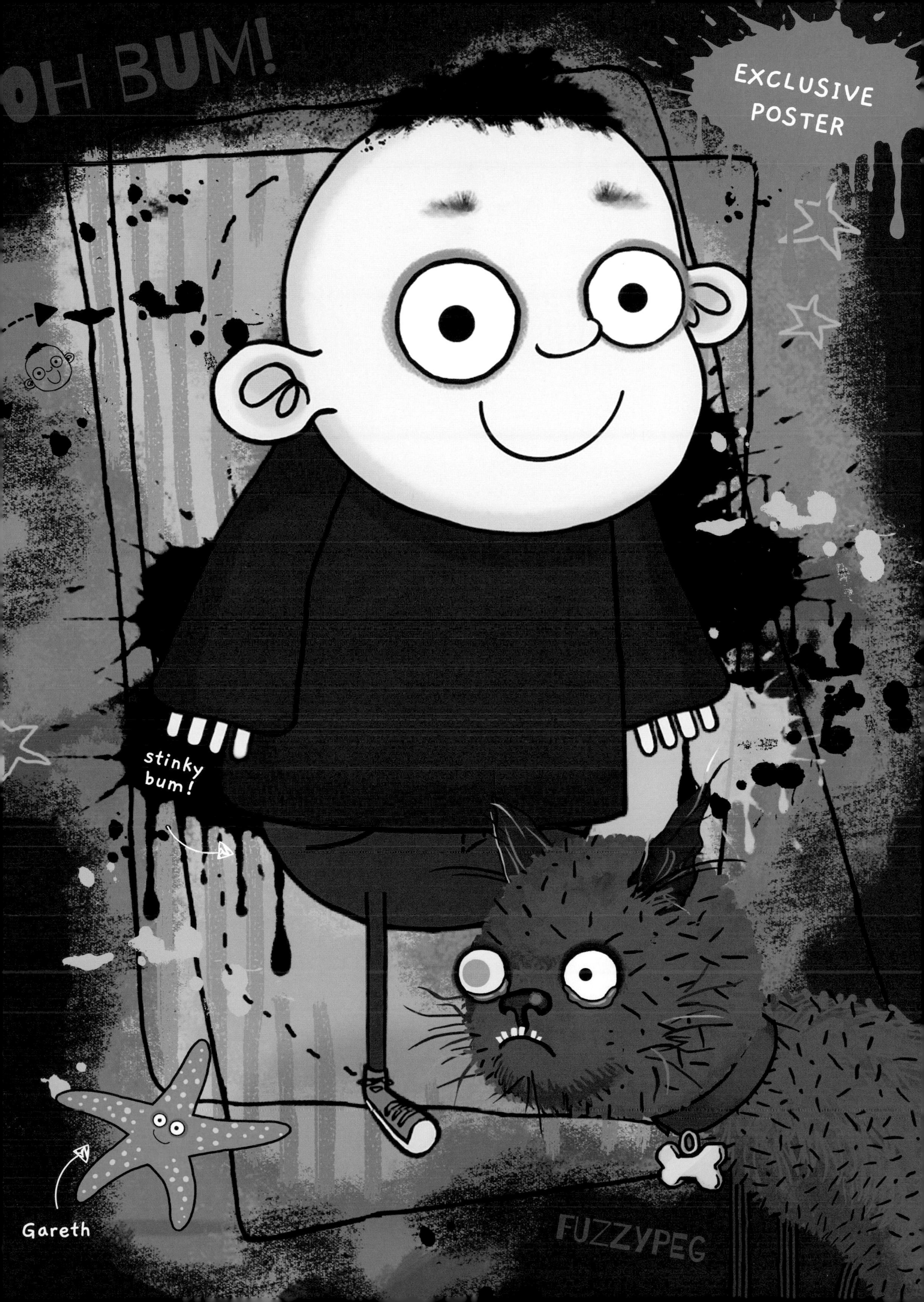
OH BUM!
EXCLUSIVE POSTER
stinky bum!
Gareth
FUZZYPEG

GRAN'S HEAD SCRATCHER

Gran loves a puzzle! See if you can solve her clues faster than a whippet with wind!

Bog off.

Stop that naughty Granny!

DOWN

1. Fuzzypeg eats this, but Gran doesn't mind sharing (3,4)
2. Breaking wind in the camper is strictly ___ (9)
4. George Spud loves to save ___ (5)
5. Dave's room smells just like a mouldy Brussels ___ (6)

ACROSS

3. Dave's weird undead friend is called ___ Katie (6)
6. Grimsby's magnet of disaster and Gran's grandson! (4,4)
7. Gran always says, 'Remember – do it with ___!' (5)

The answers are on P68

43

DAVE'S CRUSH

The Spud family live her[e]

THIS TASTES FUNNY.

1 At the Spuds' flat, everyone was tucking into a healthy meal of tinned sprouts. Dave's tin was unmarked and tasted funny. 'The tins without labels were in the dog food aisle, Dave,' said Anna smugly.

2 'Oh, BUM!' Dave left to go and brush his teeth. Dave never brushed his teeth without being asked! The suprising event caused shock waves to radiate out from Grimsby Heights into space.

44

3 As soon as Dave finished brushing his teeth, the doorbell rang. Dave opened the front door. Standing there was a girl who smelled like cheese and onion crisps (in a nice way). Dave was speechless — who was this?

4

'I'm Chuffy Peaches,' she said. She tried to sell Dave a loo brush. Dave went redder than a monkey's bum and slammed the door. His family teased him about his new special friend.

5

Dave couldn't stop thinking about Chuffy. Gareth convinced him to give her a present. The only problem was that Dave had no money.

6

Dave fished around the back of the sofa to find some cash. He found some loo roll, an old sock, a tin can, a dead rodent and some pants, but no coins. Maybe Chuffy would like his sofa treasure?

OI DAVE...

What can possibly go wrong?!

7

Dave ran to find the wagon Chuffy sold her loo brushes from. His family were already there to watch! Chuffy was delighted with her present.

Betty offered to look after Chuffy's wagon, so she and Dave could have fun. Dave and Chuffy strolled past the wild coat that lived by the bins and down the canal full of shopping trolleys. It was dead romantic.

8

9

DAVE'S A DONKEY

Meanwhile, Anna couldn't resist pressing a button or two in Chuffy's strangely high-tech bog brush wagon. One activated a laser gun on the roof, and the other made them float in mid-air. Weird, eh?

10

46

Dave was showing Chuffy his favourite skip to play in. 'Things aren't rubbish when I'm with you,' he said. 'I can be my real self around you, Dave Spud,' said Chuffy. Then she turned into an alien that looked freakily like a loo brush! OH BUM!

11 Dave took Chuffy back to her wagon. The Spuds learned that Chuffy had come to turn Earth into a giant toilet. Thousands of her alien friends were on their way to help!

Getting drenched is rubbish!

12 Dave sadly told Chuffy that she had better leave. But later that night, the night sky filled with spaceships leaving Earth again. Chuffy had saved the day by telling the aliens Earth was a bit well, rubbish.

13 Dave was pleased that Chuffy could stay with them in Grimsby Heights. Betty was even more pleased: she had Dave's alien girlfriend to replace her loo brush!

SHADOW SHAPES

ANSWERS

1. _____
2. _____
3. _____
4. _____
5. _____
6. _____
7. _____
8. _____
9. _____
10. _____
11. _____
12. _____
13. _____
14. _____

48

HONKING

gareth

stinky bum

RAT DOG...

meet
FUZZYPEG

FACT FILE
NAME: Fuzzypeg
NICKNAME: Stinky Little
Rat Dog.
BREED: Part Yorkshire terrier,
part mongrel, part fart-machine.
FAVOURITE HUMAN: Dave Spud. He adopted
Fuzzypeg when he found him living in a bin.
FAVOURITE FOOD: Anything
LEAST FAVOURITE THING: Baths.
His fleas hate them too.

DID YOU KNOW? Fuzzypeg is so full of gas, he can breathe in space!

PATCH IT UP

Oh Bum! Fuzzypeg got hold of Dave's photo and now it's in tatters! Can you piece it together in the right order?

1

2

3

4

5

The answers are on P68

Answer: ....

51

FUZZYPEG
in Space

1 Something stranger than usual was happening in Grimsby. The washing machine clicked onto its spin cycle. It began to rattle and shake, spinning so fast...

...that a giant BLACK HOLE opened up behind it!

2 Meanwhile, Dave was happily playing Fuzzypeg. Then the whole family marche[d] into his room and be[gan] to blame the poor do[g] for stealing their stu[ff.]

3 Betty put Fuzzypeg in the kitchen while they looked for their missing stuff. As soon as the door was closed, the old mutt was pulled towards the black hole! He whimpered as he flew into the dark vortex.

4 Dave heard Fuzzypeg's cries and came to check on him. He discovered the hole. OH BUM! Dave quickly hatched a plan to get his dog back.

The universe can sniff my pants!

5 Dave was soon dressed in flippers and a wetsuit with an oxygen tank on his back. Then he tumbled into the hole and landed in space. The items everyone had lost floated past, and so did FUZZYPEG!

YOU SAVED ME, DAVE

6 Dave looked at his stinky best friend and thought of how they met. Dave had been picking a burger off the floor, when a smelly rat dog leapt out of a bin and grabbed it. When the tug of war had ended, Dave had decided to take the smelly dog home.

'Tea time!' called Betty from back in the kitchen. But Dave didn't want to leave Fuzzypeg floating in space, so the Spuds wheeled out a food trolley and some camping gear and floated over for a zero-gravity picnic.

7

8

George never missed the chance of a free holiday. He pitched a tent and they all settled down to sleep. Then... Uh-oh, gravity was pulling them down to Earth!

THAT LOOKS HOT DAVE!

9

But Dave still wouldn't leave his dog. He grabbed Fuzzypeg and they fell for miles, burning up like a slice of toast. The rest of the Spuds watched as tiny fragments of Dave and Fuzzypeg floated down through the air.

10 Luckily, the clouds had a plan. They gobbled up all of the tiny pieces and began to perform an ancient ritual, chanting and dancing in the air. Then they spat out a brand-new Dave and Fuzzypeg!

11 Dave and Fuzzypeg fell from the clouds and splashed down in the lake, followed by all the missing stuff from their flat. Dave looked up and thanked the clouds, who simply winked and pooped out a shoe.

12 The shoe was big enough for Dave and Fuzzypeg to climb in and row to shore. But why were the Spuds suddenly so massive? Oh, BUM! The clouds had remade Dave and Fuzzypeg to be the size of snowflakes. RUBBISH!

tiny Dave

SOUND LIKE
TROUBLE TO YOU?

SPD_OI

meet
THE TWINS

Twin

FACT FILE

NAMES: The Twins don't have names yet. The Spuds just call them Twin A and Twin B.

GENDER: Undecided

FAVOURITE FOOD: Curry

FAVOURITE THING: Everything! But especially Fuzzypeg.

LEAST FAVOURITE THING: Goldfish, especially Funny Fins.

DID YOU KNOW? The twins are learning to say a few different words now.

56

EVERYONE ON THE PLANE

1 START HERE

2 KNICKERS! You forgot Gran! Go back to the start.

3

12 TYPICAL! Sucked into a black hole. Go back 3 spaces.

11

10

13

14 DONKEY CHOPS! Gran forgot her teeth. GO BACK TO THE START!

15 George goes to the tip. Miss a turn.

WOO! YOU MADE IT!

23

22

Look – I can see the plane!

Take it in turns to roll the dice and move your counter the amount of spaces you roll. The first to get to the plane wins, but a Spud family outing wouldn't be complete without a few disasters!

4 I HAVE A PLAN! Slide down the lamp to number 8.

5

EEK! You dodge Zombie Katie. ROLL AGAIN! **6**

9 Anna's 'UNGRY. GO BACK 4 spaces to get chips

8

SNACK! Have a donut! GO TO 20! **7**

16

17 CRACKING! Found free stuff in a skip. ROLL AGAIN!

18

21 EVACUATE! The dog's gonna explode! Go back to 3.

20

19 BUM! It starts to rain. Miss a turn.

meet
ROBERT ROBOT

FACT FILE

FAVOURITE THINGS: Robert loves to dance, usually like a Robot!
FAVOURITE FOOD: His mum veggie sausage rolls.
DISLIKES: Removing his box head, and reading because the words go all jumbly.
FUN FACT: Robert's Box head is a mystery – it's a very special box and not everything in it makes sense.

meet
LIL' SUE

FACT FILE

LIKES: Being an entrepreneur. Among other jobs, she has worked as an airline pilot, a supermarket cashier, a bus driver, a tour guide and she has owned a hot dog van!
DISLIKES: People wasting her time.
FUN FACT: Lil' Sue has a sister called Lil' Sue's Lil' Sis.

WE ARE NOT DOING IT...

Our friend Dave Spud

meet
ZOMBIE KATIE

FACT FILE

LIKES: Chewing on things.
DISLIKES: When her limbs fall off, though she can reattach them if needed.
FAVOURITE ACTIVITY: Playing golf.
Favourite food: Banana custard and pizza.
FUN FACT: Katie lives in a caravan with her father, Donald, who adopted her.

Sports day. Go team green!

IT SMELLS OF WEE!!!!!

yuck!

61

DAVE'S BIKE FRIGHT

That's rubbis

1 Anna had turned the kitchen into a racetrack. She was practising for her cycling test. Dave didn't have a bike! But George had a surprise up his sleeve: he'd made one!

ZOOM!!!

2 Dave was over the moon until he saw the bike. George called it 'the upcycle'. He'd made it out of stuff from the tip. There was even a bucket for Dave to wear as a helmet.

At school, on the day of the bike test, Dave, Anna and their friends all took it in turns to navigate the course.

4

Robert Robot knocked the cones over and Lil Sue crashed into a tree.

OH DEAR DAVE!

Anna did well. She zipped through the track before tumbling out of her wheelchair.

5

6

Dave had a go, but his bike brakes were made of old toothbrushes. When doing an emergency stop test, Dave pulled on the brakes and couldn't stop! He crashed into Anna who flew into the air and landed on his handlebars.

63

7

Dave still couldn't stop! He rode out of Grimsby and down south through the country, all the way to the white cliffs of Dover...

8

... where Dave and Anna sped off the cliff. WOOOSH! They flew over the channel and crashed onto French soil.

9

It was up to Betty to save her beloved darlings! She piled the family into the camper and drove off after them.

HOW ARE WE GOING TO FIND THEM?

OOH LA LA

9 Meanwhile, Dave and Anna had somehow wound up in the last leg of the Tour de France. Dave was even in the lead! Next stop: Paris!

10 Hot on their trail, the Spuds rolled off the ferry and caught up with the upcycle. Betty leant out of the camper like an action movie star. She snatched Anna and dragged her to safety but Dave was still stuck on the upcycle. How could he stop?

11 'Oi, buckethead!' called Gran. She CHUCKED a crusty baguette into Dave's spokes. The upcycle stalled, Dave flew over the handles and sailed through the winning line. He'd just won the Tour de France!

DAVE'S QUIZ

This should prove entertaining.

1 WHO ELSE DID DAVE MEET AT THE BOTTOM OF THE SEA WHEN HE FIRST MET GARETH?
a. A whale
b. An octopus
c. A donkey called Kevin

2 WHAT DOES ANNA SAY SHE'S REALLY GOOD AT?
a. Popping a wheelie
b. Annoying Dave
c. Eating chips

3 WHAT'S THE NAME OF DAVE'S ALIEN GIRLFRIEND?
a. Chuffy Peaches
b. Fluffy Beaches
c. Buffy Leeches

4 WHAT COUNTRY DOES DAVE LAND IN ON HIS 'UPCYCLE' BIKE?
a. Wales
b. China
c. France

5 WHAT DOES GEORGE'S BROKEN WASHING MACHINE CREATE IN THE KITCHEN?
a. A white elephant
b. A black hole
c. A green monster

6 WHERE DOES GEORGE SPUD WORK?
a. The chippy
b. The dump
c. The bank

7 WHAT'S ODD ABOUT DAVE'S MATE ROBERT?
a. He's a yeti
b. He's a giant
c. He's a robot

8 WHAT DOES ANNA'S HAIRSLIDE LOOK LIKE?
a. A skull
b. A bin lorry
c. A cute, fluffy bunny

9 COMPLETE GRAN'S FAVOURITE SAYING: 'DO IT WITH...'
a. Gravy!
b. Gusto!
c. Goop!

10 WHEN LIFE GETS YOU DOWN—BETTY LIKES TO...
a. Have a fry up
b. Have a nap
c. Have a disco!

Spuds united!

HOW DID YOU DO?

The answers are on P68

LOADS OF ANSWERS

P16. Who You Looking At?

1. Anna, 2. Gran, 3. Dave, 4. Fuzzypeg,
8. Lil' Sue, 6. George, 7. Gareth,
9. Betty, 10. Twin A (or Twin B!)

P19. Dot-to-Dot

A falling whale

P23. Odd One Out

Crikey! That page is full of imposters! So we've come to hang out here!

P24. Puzzled?

1-C, 2-H, 3-J, 4-G, 5-N, 6-M, 7-K,
8-L, 9-D, 10-A, 11-E, 12-I, 13-F, 14-B

P31. Spot the Difference

P32. Help Dave Escape

P34. Look And Find

Gran●, The Twins●, Gareth●, Fuzzypeg●,
Betty●, George●, Camper , Robert Robot,
Apple Core●, 13 Packs of Pink Loo Roll●,
5 Individual White Loo Rolls●, 4 x Pairs
of Underwear●

P37. Find Them!

The hidden word is TOILET

P43. Gran's Head Scratcher

DOWN: 1. Dog Food, 2. Forbidden, 4. Money, 5.
Sprout. ACROSS: 3. Zombie, 6. Dave Spud, 7.
Gusto

Pg48. Shadow Shapes

1. Gareth, 2. Anna, 3. Betty, 4. Zombie Katie,
5. Robert Robot, 6. Couch, 7. Doughnut,
8. The Twins, 9. Dave, 10. George,
11. Fuzzypeg, 12. Lil'Sue, 13. Toilet, 14.Camper

P51. Patch it Up

The order from top to bottom is: 5, 2, 1, 4, 3

P57. Who Said That?

A-Dave, B-Anna, C-Gran, D-Gareth,
E-George, F-Betty

P66. Dave's Quiz

1-B, 2-A, 3-A, 4-C, 5-B, 6-B, 7-C, 8-A,
9-B, 10-C